SL

YOU'RE GONNA WANNA HEAR THIS

AM!

SL

YOU'RE GONNA WANNA HEAR THIS

AM!

CHOSEN BY NIKITA GILL

MACMILLAN

For every poet.
Your voice is valued.

First published 2020 by Macmillan Children's Books
a division of Macmillan Publishers Limited
The Smithson, 6 Briset Street, London EC1M 5NR
Basingstoke and Oxford
Associated companies throughout the world
www.panmacmillan.com

ISBN 978-1-529-02830-0

1 3 5 7 9 8 6 4 2

A CIP catalogue record for this book is available from the British Library.

Printed and bound by CPI Group (UK) Ltd, Croydon CR0 4YY

INTRODUCTION BY NIKITA GILL

All poetry is real poetry.

Walk into a room and ask anyone for their definition of poetry. No two people will be able to give you the same answer. Poetry's become the fastest growing art form in Britain and that isn't just from traditional poets or from printed collections. It is in no small part due to the resilient and powerful work of performance poets and spoken word artists. And slams are the platform that have allowed for this growth.

A slam, for those who do not know, is a competition where poets perform their verse on stage in a set amount of time and are marked by judges from the audience, or sometimes guest judges. Judges take into account many things; audience reaction, the delivery, and the beauty of the verse: it's about connecting with an audience and letting them in on a secret.

When I write poems, I approach the mediums I place them on with equal importance – whether I put them on a blog, on Instagram or submit them to literary journals. It never occurred to me that posting my work in a certain medium would mean I would then be defined by that medium. This is why I find such a kinship with performance-based poets.

To define a poet who performs their work as a 'slam poet', and to suggest that 'slam poets' aren't 'real poets' is a myopic misrepresentation of the work they do. There is no such thing as slam poetry – simply poetry that works in slams. There are no slam poets, only poets who, with immense craft, have the added skill of performing their work in a way that enthralls an audience. One kind of poetry is not superior to another due to the format it is produced or shared in.

For years, poetry has been misconceived as an area of elite literature which is for the privileged few to craft, learn or teach a certain way. It has been sequestered to the classroom as something that made us groan as we studied and peeled layer after layer off Milton's work in an attempt to understand just what he meant.

But what if there was a different version of poetry? What if we let it out of the classroom and put it on stage? What if poetry is remembered to be what it is: the language of fire, fury and freedom? What if, and bear with me, poetry was for everyone again?

This is exactly what performance poetry is about. It reminds us of the revolution poetry incites. People from all walks of life flock to venues or YouTube to watch their favourite poets perform on stage, using language they can relate to, incorporating humour with tragedy in an almost Shakespearean way. Slams are an inclusive, open space, giving poets from under-represented communities a supportive environment to share their truth, and presenting it in a format so easily accessible and unpretentious, that people who'd never engaged with poetry before are finally able to.

This book is a manifesto for change in many ways. It is a manifesto for performance poetry, the craft and beauty of it and the way it resonates with millions of people. It is a manifesto for poetry itself, as poets are natural truth-tellers and bring us face to face with honesty in a time where fact is being dismissed for opinion. It is a manifesto for compassion and how important it is in a world that is ever more divided.

The poets in this book are awe-inspiring. Their work is transcendent, both on the stage and on the page. Without them, poetry would not be what it is today: empowering, immensely emotive, approachable, wise, humorous – and all of this whilst being stunningly and thoughtfully constructed.

Each of the poems in this book is a gift of truth. From the anthem that is Raymond Antrobus's 'Dear Hearing World' to the tenderness of Jinhao Xie's '妳好/Hello', these voices are urgent and they deserve to be heard.

But enough from me. As it has been said by our ancestors in art, let the work speak for itself. Allow these words to wash over you and sit with you. Speak them out loud, so the truth rings loud and clear. Digest the power of this book slowly the way I did the first time I read it.

After all, poetry is not a luxury, certainly not in the world we live in today. It is a war cry – a battle song. And you're gonna wanna hear this.

I hope you find what you are looking for in these pages.

With verse, warmth and love,

Nikita.

CONTENTS

HOME

KIN

DUALITY

PROTEST

DESIRE

ACCEPTANCE

HOME

The word 'home' causes such deep-rooted connotations for every person. It transcends countries, continents, towns and cities. In this powerful first section, we get a glimpse into the many meanings of home through the eyes of the poets.

BOX

by Rakaya Fetuga

I wrote this poem at a workshop run by Sukina Pilgrim, so it came from a place of play and experimenting. Each of us in the room imagined ourselves as the spokesperson for a whole group of people. Searching for a voice to represent all black African British women was unifying but also lacking and confining, as labels are. Here is 'Box'.

I am the bougie plantain skewers and sweet chilli dip chicks.
The third generation, more lost than the second
but free enough to write poems about it.
I am the girls who wear ankara headwraps to work
that dazzle Jane and Paul from HR.
I am the black girls who have never seen African soil,
have never run on golden sand
the girls whose homeland is just a figment
of their imagination
or just the pigment in their skin
and I'm the girls who go back home all the time
the ones who basically live there too
the African village girls
the African city girls
the African Queen – of a town in Kumasi as big
as Harlesden girls

1

I am the natural hair movement sisters
the bantu knot flat twisters
the 'our hair is versatile, relax and weave'
the 'I paid for this hair so it's mine, best believe'.
I'm the don't touch my hair.
I'm the whip it back and forth in my living room
hijab in the street hunnies.
I am the Melanin Mamis.
I'm the Fuse and Wiz Kid shoki shakers
the rock and K-Pop fans,
the showing-off-but-it's-alright Drake-rs
I'm the music is harams.
I'm the post-colonial studies
the gotta make that money-monies
the black business, black love, black girl magic
black don't crack chanters.
I'm the 'do I still count as black?' African girls,
the 'my parents are African, I'm British' girls.
I am the lost my mother-tongue in a burgundy book
a Brexit soft-back that is changing its colours
this country changes its colours to us every season
rejecting its own children:
us apple crumble Supermalt sippers
us silver hoops socks and slippers
us multi-heritage, polyglot
us loud us feisty us sassy – us not
us who tick 'Black British dash African'
a square smaller than a fingernail
that our persons are layered into

I am just trying to pull back the skin of that like an onion
to find out what's inside
this one bulb of the earth
will make thousands of recipes.

Rakaya Fetuga is a performance poet and winner of the Roundhouse Poetry Slam 2018 and the Spread the Word Poetry Prize 2017. Her work joins conversations on overlapping identities, faith and cultural practice as self-affirmation. As well as performing across the UK and internationally, Rakaya has shared her poetry at Trafalgar Square, the Royal Albert Hall, the Ivy and the British Museum among other London venues and at spoken word nights. Rakaya has been commissioned by Bloomberg with Vanity Fair, the English Touring Theatre and Kyra TV and has worked in partnership with Apple for the Made in London workshop series. Rakaya is a Roundhouse Resident Artist and her monodrama *Unbraided* is showing as part of the Last Word Festival 2020. Her poem 'Enterprise' was published in *Letters to the Earth* (Harper Collins, 2019). Rakaya is a member of ::nana:: Poetry Collective.

TOP TIP: Everyone has their own way of bringing words to life on stage – if you're like me, memorize your poem and let go of your notebook safety net. Performing at its best feels like telling my friends a story when I'm getting to the juicy bit. In a way, we perform every day. So breathe deep, talk slow and smile – enjoy it!

SARGAM

by Fathima Zahra

Sargam was the name of the biggest expat community events when I was growing up in Jeddah. It is also a letter away from meaning heaven in Malayalam.

I mishear my friend say she went to heaven for the weekend/ how there were string lights everywhere/ how they danced all night/ how her parents lost their frowns in the crowd/ I asked her why she left/ I was six/ God knows I don't still picture Jannah the way I did/ when the class prefect tries her best sermon pitch/ 'you know Al-Baik?/ you get those in heaven/ anything you love/ comes flying to you'/ there's never been a version of heaven that didn't hold my old life/ of datepalms and corniche picnics/ where the sun squeezed our headaches alive/ ordered shawarma from the Lebanese diner/ of all the things I said goodbye to/ loss slept in the house coated by sand/ where we watched the world from a periscope/ our days punctuated by the Adhan/ I've downsized my duas since/ they exchange outfits at the gates of heaven/ asks to be let in/ asks about a boy/ a dead grandfather/ of all the heavens I've hoarded/ I like the one with the flying boxes of fried chicken best/ the one where the bouncer speaks arabic/ where I don't need the right passport to stay

Fathima Zahra is an Indian poet currently based in Essex. She is a Barbican Young Poet and a Roundhouse Poetry Collective alum. Her work has been featured across BBC World News, the *New Indian Express* and Young Poets Network. She has won the Bridport Prize, Wells Festival of Literature Young Poets Award and Asia House Poetry Slam 2019. In her work, she tends to explore the lives of the diaspora and what belonging means to her. She is currently studying towards a Biomedical Sciences degree at Queen Mary University of London.

TOP TIP: I learned this from my mentor Shantanu Anand, and it has transformed the way I prepare for a slam. Bring the audience into the room when you practise, picture faces of your loved ones, poets you look up to, strangers; each time you step into the space, picture invoking a different reaction in the audience and get on with your poem. That way, when you go on stage, no matter what happens, you can tell yourself, 'I've done this before'!

MY CITY AND I

by Xinyue Jiang

This was written alongside an English assignment with the prompt 'loss', but it's instead about rediscovery. This poem is about how they can be, and often are, the same thing.

we meet like a pair of old lovers, my city and I.

ni qu na er le? the streetlights are saying
(where have you been?)
in the morse code I memorised at seven.
wei shen me zhe me jiu dou bu hui lai?
(why have you been gone so long?)
so much has changed since you've been gone.

I know, I know, my love,
I answer as I watch the taxis drive past on the boulevard.
and I asked you to wait for me, all those years ago.

wo deng le, she says.
(I waited)
I waited through all the mian-ao winters
and the bing-qi-ling summers
and the zhong-qiu-jie autumns.

wo ye deng le, I say.
(I waited too)
I waited for all those foreign-dollar paychecks
and that single one o'clock morning flight back home.

Home, she says.
wo xiang ni le, lao tou
(I missed you, old man)
even with the white winter beard.

wo ye xiang ni le, I tell her.
wo men qu shui jiao ba;
wo yao da shi cha.
(let's go to bed;
I need to sleep off the jetlag.)

Xinyue Jiang is a sixteen year old sixth form student in Cambridgeshire who writes too much and sleeps too little. 'my city and i' was a Foyle Young Poet commended poem. FYP is run by The Poetry Society.

> **TOP TIP:** Be passionate and write/speak about anything that inspires you and then some things that don't.

AMONGST THE SMOG

by Tanaka Fuego

This is a poem that explores the suffocation so many Londoners feel and sometimes can't put into words, going further than the packed trains and alluding to the pollution that is killing us everyday.

(Sung)

ISN'T this city so pretty
ISN'T this something to see
I said ISN'T this city so pretty
ISN'T it something to see.
I'll let the grey consume me
Since there's nothing to save me

(Spoken)

ISN'T THIS CITY A SIGHT FOR SORE EYES
I MEAN
A contributing factor for sore throats
I mean
ISN'T THIS CITY A KILLER.
Something of an inferno
Or maybe a tsunami

Isn't this city built like a vacuum
Holding on to all the grey
All the smog
Correct me if I'm wrong
But I think Britain has attachment issues
Cause we can't seem to let go of all that's
Killing us
And if it won't be the water
Then I'm sure it will be the air

So as I said
ISN'T THIS CITY A SIGHT FOR SORE EYES
A contributing factor for sore throats
I mean
ISN'T THIS CITY A KILLER.

Got all of us and these kids in a choke hold
Dancing around the fire which is
This countries burning
And don't we all sleep so well
Accustomed to the taste of death
Dancing in our mouths
Yet how can we complain
When all we know is pollution
When all we know is the scent of tomorrow's yesterday
When all we know is how to surrender
To the grey.

I've had visions that one day oxygen tanks would fall from the sky.
This country will call it a Gift
I will call it a lifeline
The First taste of salvation
A breath of fresh air
Something I've craved my whole existence
But how can you miss something you've never had.

(Sung)

ISN'T this city so pretty
ISN'T this something to see
I said ISN'T this city so pretty
ISN'T it something to see.
I'll let the grey consume me
Since there's nothing to save me.

Tanaka also known as Tanaka.fuego is a slam-winning, multi-published, international spoken word artist, who has performed to sold-out shows at Edinburgh's Fringe festival. He is a BBC 1xtra Words First alum and a Roundhouse Poetry Slam finalist, alongside being commissioned by the BBC. He is a Black queer artist whose poems cross leaps and boundaries throughout his Identity.

TOP TIP: Don't forget to center yourself. Take a few deep breaths and remind yourself why you're even doing this.

NOT DYING FOR LONDON

after 'What Are We' by Jeremiah Brown

by Troy Cabida

'Not dying for London' is in response to the extreme levels of exhaustion living in the city can have on us and how that can be received through the lens of a young Filipino person who's just trying to get to work on time and not lose an arm over heartache, racism and buses that go on diversion.

not   as in growing older/as in growing in the right tempo/as in their tempo, not mine/as in a tightness around my stomach/as in exhales that do nothing/as in denial/as in resistance as a physical form of denial/as in this isn't what should be defined as healing

dying   as in Sunday evenings talking to a bridge/as in rejecting a hug/as in no longer believing in hugs/as in a sleeping drunk/as in your back as a symphony of cracks/as in the path I chose/as in a side effect of truth/as in a side effect of silence/as in not speaking

for   as in those in need/as in empathy/as in the lesser sibling of compassion/as in service for others/as in disservice to the self/as in going through with it/as in deflecting bullets/as in

11

by refusing my embrace, whose heart are you really protecting

London   as in white woman shoulder bumping into me/
as in strong pace to deflect white woman shoulder bumping into
me/as in every day delay/as in every day diverted/as in blind when
rainy but blinding when sunny/as in weather trying to kill me/as
in a city trying to kill me/as in a city trying to toughen me up/as
in a city trying to kill me/as in a city failing

Troy Cabida (b. 1995) is a London-based Filipino poet. He has
been a member of the Barbican Young Poets, the Roundhouse
Poetry Collective and is a producer for open mic night Poetry and
Shaah. His poems have appeared in *TAYO*, *harana*, *Bukambibig*,
Cha and Ink, and *Sweat and Tears*. His debut pamphlet, *War Dove*,
was published by Bad Betty Press in 2020.

TOP TIP: As creatives, we're fortunate to undertake work
that can leave us satisfied professionally but also healed
emotionally and connected with the world. With that, is a
level of reality that you have to be aware of, so the work that
comes out is substantial and can stand on its own. Whether
that's working in a collective, performing at a slam or simply
editing a friend's early draft, always remember to have fun
but also to treat poetry as a job that can have stability and
longevity.

LANGUAGE

by Duranka Perera

As a Sri Lankan living in the UK's diaspora, there's a certain prestige assigned by our elders to those who can speak their mother tongue. To do so helps us connect with our history in the most intimate of ways. This makes it hard for people like me who have never lived in Sri Lanka long-term, and thus never had the consistent exposure to the language that our parents had. That said, it is never too late to learn and connect, and this poem is all about that process of building the confidence to do so.

Oyage katahanda ingrisi lamayek wage
She said, just a joke.
But that joke echoes through every generation
That grows up abroad,
Cutting bingawal through ugurawal
As engollange diwal struggle to reconnect
To the language
With which their families painted home.

Our lives here are different,
Coloured by influences that
On all too frequent occasions,
Would make our achchis weep.

That your language can only be spoken fluently
By friends who lived there as children
Might whiten your tongue even further
Than your parents say it has become.

But some things stay the same.

Whenever you hear someone talk about the cricket, you think
    machang.
Whenever you hear someone tell the jokes your cousin does, you
    think aiya.
Whenever you hear someone speak the language of your ancestors,
    even as much as you doubt yourself,
You think pawla.

It doesn't matter how much you know now.
It doesn't matter how you sound.
It matters that you care.
That you're willing to pick up that potha,
Put on Bathiya and Santhush,
Talk to your seeya once in a while about the life he made,
In the tongue he made it with.

Language is not a barrier, but a road,
So strengthen that tongue of yours my friend.
Your journey is about to unfold.

Duranka Perera is a doctor based in the East of England. After binge-watching *Avatar: The Last Airbender* in secondary school, he became bewitched by writing's capacity to create worlds, worlds rich in life and emotion, be they fantastic or otherwise. This sparked him on a journey that culminated in founding a writing society at his university, where he could and continues to bring like-minded souls together to encourage each other through their craft. His writing, enriched by his Sri Lankan heritage and strongly held belief in diversity, seeks to embody life's great variety. To him, the world is a writing sandbox: one where no story deserves to be left untold. His aspiration is to become a surgeon and author in the vein of Henry Marsh and Atul Gawande, though he is well aware that he has a long way to go before being as cool as either.

TOP TIP: The art of slam is to connect with your own words and to help others do the same. The best tip for learning how to perform poetry therefore can be split into two parts – first, find your own voice, and then watch how other performers get the most out of theirs. Watch for pauses, enunciation, physicality. See what works for you to help make the most out of your performance.

LOST IN TRANSLATION

by Aman Grover

This poem delves into the sometimes convoluted relationship we share with our culture and heritage, and the journey to understanding it better and embodying its true values.

A wide-eyed, gora-looking bacha, about yay high,
In his mud-infused cardigan and forest-green eyes,
With a fixed look of marvel and love for the way,
The world around could enlighten, enchant and mesmerise.

Year 3. World History. He sat quite still, for lasting fear,
That moving would mean missing another word,
Transfixed as the supply teacher, lost in soliloquy,
Spoke of Pyramids and Great Walls and aboriginal herds.

What followed was a fleeting moment, a blink in time,
The kind that would fizzle and pass you by,
If you didn't sense the weight of my Bharat's delta plains,
And millennia of farmers with no tears left to cry.

'Who here knows the name of the longest and most famous river in India?'

Miss Birch's voice echoed across the classroom,
Something warm in my insides flitted and pranced,
It rose and came to rest between my shoulder blades,
Lovers reunited for one final dance.

'I know, Miss Birch! Pick me, pick me. India's most famous river is
  called the Ganga!'

After all, I'd been told the story for as long as I can remember.

Fresh from an evening of battling with my shower hair,
With generous helpings of Vatika and the like-clockwork sigh,
Maa would beckon me over, from her spot on that sofa,
Scoop me up in her weary arms and cradle me high.

Her words, oh, how they fell,
Delicately poised, quivering yet strong, fragrant and true,
Like garam malai in the leftover kheer,
Stories descended, first father then daughter, now son and you.

In hushed tones she spoke, as though the brevity of her words,
May swallow her whole if left unspoken.
Of the day Shiva began to sing, melodious,
And not a heart was left unopened.

Something in Vishnu stirred, drowning out his senses,
A tide washing out without the promise of returning,
It pervaded every part of his mind,

With a sense of belonging and yearning.

At once he began to melt, dissolve,
As though the song had emulated rebirth,
When Brahma caught the molten Vishnu,
And redirected him onto our Earth – hamara (our) Ganga.

'But Maa, it's just a river.'

She smiled, that kind of smile, where one knew,
In the winding canyons of Yamuna that hollowed the wrinkles of
    her cheeks.
In her parched skin, barren plains with eons of half-fulfilled
    dreams.
The light in her eyes dancing, with Rajasthan ka rang and
    Kashmir's khushboo.

Ganga nourished and nurtured our Mother Earth,
Replenishing her vessel, sating her thirst.
To bathe in the waters, life-giving and pure,
Is to surrender one's soul in God and endure.

*'I'm afraid you're incorrect, Aman. You must be mistaken, it's
    pronounced the Ganges.'*

Ancestral whispers, the fidget of restless heads,
My identity reaped in the seeds newly sown,
Reminiscing childhood stories and morning aartis (prayers),
As Hindustan's withered complexion reflected in my own.

Oh Ganga, redeemer of the fallen, mother of my salvation,
Help me unravel this conflicted heritage of mine,
Through the winding Sindhu Valley you may trace my lineage,
My blood coursing through these banks, tales through the
    grapevine.

Upon the cobbled steps of Banaras,
Silhouettes meditating, immersed in the milky saffron waters,
Boats perched amongst the marigold garlands,
A mother, cradling trembling ashes, mumbling her mantras.

Pilgrims descend in their masses,
Orphan hearts seeking blissful rest,
Mother and giver of refuge,
Starlings flocking westwards, returning to your nest.

You flow from the Himalaya, down through Kashi,
Kaash (wish), I wish to understand your divine influence,
For is there a river as wretched and cursed,
As to carry and cleanse my people's afflictions.

Oh Ganga, grant me liberation,
Bless my broken British tongue and ail my impurities.
Through your ebbs and flows, channel strength of mind,
So I may wear upon my armour, my Bharat's true qualities.

The word is Ganga, my friend
Sweet wine of compassion, Holy Mother.
More than just a river, liquid Shakti (strength),

19

Uniting Hindustanis as brothers.

For no child is too dirty to be embraced by his Mother.
No child too spirited to be without your watchful gaze.
The word is Ganga, my friend,
That's OK, I'll allow you to rephrase.

Aman Grover (b. 1995) is a public speaker and spoken word artist based in Hounslow. His poetry often reflects on the rich mixing pot of culture, identity and faith that represents being a British Asian. He's driven by creating an impact in his local communities, whether that is through facilitating education workshops for students across London or studying for his Master's degree in Climate Change.

> **TOP TIP:** Remembering that I have a unique voice and worthwhile message that can resonate with even one member of the audience helps calm my nerves. Then I focus on giving my all for that one.

ENG/LAND

OR THOUGHTS AFTER THINKING ABOUT BUYING AN 'ENGLAND' BUCKET HAT AHEAD OF THE 2018 WORLD CUP SEMI-FINAL MATCH AGAINST CROATIA

by Bridget Minamore

I wrote this poem in the week between the quarter- and semi-finals of the 2018 World Cup, and I've barely changed it since. It feels very much of the moment – it was a sweltering July, the media was rabid with the possibility of sporting glory, but more surprisingly, loads of my friends were too. I've always loved football, so grappled with my iffy feelings around the intersections between English nationalism, football fanaticism, and being a Black female football fan a long time ago. Seeing my mates – of all class and race backgrounds – get more invested in the World Cup than me was so bizarre. I tried to put that 'bizarre' feeling into a poem, and here we are.

England

      Eng/land

            Eng / land   is a word that gets
            caught in my throat
                      cannot find a clean way through me—
                          I can't say it without a stumble
                so I break it down / carve it up,

split it into two / it's only fair to do to it what it does to me, too;

      Eng/land
              Eng / land

Land of eating bland food when it's not from another land

Land of rain, rain, go away

Land of vans / land of white and GO HOME OR FACE
ARREST vans

Land of lions / three they say / three lions for a country
                      too cold for them anyway

Land of football / *home* of football—home of my love for football
            despite all these thoughts I wish I didn't have
              when thinking about the word Eng/land

Home of buying overpriced, sweatshop-made England football tat
whilst still flinching at overpriced, sweatshop-made England flags
outside my neighbours' house,

                                    Land of contradictions.
England

      Eng / land

Eng / like 'in' / like slicing off the last G in –ing English words
        like *freezin* and *jarrin* and *amazin*
            but keep a G in peng, keep a G in ting—
      keep these G's to remind you of the G's you grew up with
      not the silver spoon rich kids who say you sound *aggressive*
            No-one says pen tin to the mandem
               when describing a girl they like—
                   apart from poets.

Eng / like 'in' / like *innit bruv*
      innit being a word I hear with the same frequency
              from the boys on my dad's stairwell
                to the builders by my house
            to my mum's mates outside church;

Why do my Ghanaian Aunties like to say 'innit' so much?
Why do the builders outside say 'innit' to me as a substitute for
    good morning?
Why do I adore both groups to the point my heart hurts when I
    think of them?

Innit. In / it.

What are the boys on the stairwell actually in?

Do they feel as stuck as I once did?

Trapped by the ends and an overwhelming feeling
of both belonging to this country but
not   quite?

Eng/land

Eng / land

Home. Home? Home/land.

Home / land security style boarders around our boarders, now.

Watery boarders sharing water with watery Mediterranean graves.

Eng/land

Eng / land

Land. My / land. My land?

My sort-of land? My passport part of this land, a so-called United Kingdom of lands and my land in this kingdom is England. My home is supposedly England. Why won't England love me? How long is this complicated relationship supposed to last for—my friends are bored of me talking about England in our group chat. I hear there are others like me, too, others strung along and hoping for more. How many years can England tell me he loves me and how long am I going to feel that despite those words he wants me I still don't quite / belong?

—but for 90 minutes yesterday I felt like Eng / land was My / land

Isn't that strange? It's a small leathery ball kicked around a
rectangle of grass.

England. Eng / land. My football-loving,
hopefully World Cup winning before I die land—

You are so, so ugly to me sometimes

You are so, so ugly to everyone else, most of the time

Still. A part of me enjoys how easily I forget all of this
and somehow, someway, find this strange game

so very, very
beautiful.

Bridget Minamore is a writer from and based in South East
London. She is part of the creative team behind Brainchild
Festival and works with a project to empower women who have
experienced sexual violence. Bridget has worked with the National
Theatre and the Royal Opera House, and read her poems at places
including the Roundhouse, Latitude Festival, the Bristol Old Vic
and the Southbank Centre. In 2011 she represented the UK at
the International Biennale in Rome with Point Blank Poets, and
in 2013 was shortlisted to be London's first Young Poet Laureate.
She was chosen as one of the Hospital Club's Emerging Creatives
in 2015, and more recently, as one of Speaking Volumes 40 Stars

of Black British Literature. As a journalist, Bridget has written for publications like the *Guardian*, *Pitchfork*, *The Pool*, and *The Debrief*. She mostly writes about London, pop culture, race and feminism, as well as the intersections between them.

TOP TIP: The thing I always try to remember about writing poetry is that a poem doesn't know it's a poem. I got that from Caroline Bird, who is an amazing writer, and I say it to myself whenever I try to write. The logic in the poem needs to make sense, but at the same time, in the world of a poem, anything is possible. Poetry gives you the freedom to make up your own rules, but once you've made them, you have to stick to them. I love that.

KIN

Kin doesn't just mean the family you are born into, but also the family you make. Here, you will find how bonds are made through blood and beyond blood in language.

MONUMENTS AND PRAYER

by Karishma Sangtani

This poem was inspired by a conversation I had with my mum about our family history. It touches on the themes of grief, childhood and faith.

I drink the reflection of my mother
as conclusions undress.
She says,

'for us,
summer is always endings.'

How quickly the pit of a plum stops howling
and sits:
an offering in
bleeding air.

I trip back
into spilled gasps
and gutted planes dressed for mourning.
Perhaps God lives here –

in ghee and sugar,
in the cupped palms of loss.

I could not ask then why this season
precipitates monuments and prayer
    and monuments and prayer.
Or why it is only my right shoulder shattering.

    Instead, the evening resigns.
    I drag my breath through the dust,
    and let it hover.

Karishma Sangtani is a poet based in London and Durham whose work is often concerned with the themes of memory, family and identity. As well as featuring at events such as Heaux Noire's London Literary Festival and Bright Smoke at the Royal Shakespeare Company, she has headlined DiVerse, a monthly spoken word night in Teeside. She is currently studying for a degree in English Literature and is a member of Durham University's Slam Team.

> **TOP TIP:** Try performing your poems in front of a mirror or to close friends before a large audience.

ENOUGH

by Michelle Nathan

This poem was written after my first trip to Sri Lanka, which is
where my dad was born and grew up, before he moved to England.
It was strange travelling around a country which is a big part of
me and my heritage, and feeling unexpectedly disconnected from
it, at times. I realized that even if I couldn't speak the language,
and sometimes struggled to bond with family members, the one
thing we all had in common was food, and our love for it. So this
is an ode to family, of course, but also to food, and its almost
supernatural unifying powers.

Before I travelled to Sri Lanka
for the very first time
My cousin told me that
the most important word
I could learn in Tamil
is Kaarnum –
Enough

And I didn't understand why
until I got there

There
where each meal is so distinct
but also seem to slowly meld together –
as one ends
the preparation for the next begins

There
where they pile the plates so high
the food could almost touch the sky

There
where the edible leaning tower before me
threatens to spill over the sides and floor me
I somehow find the strength to say
'Thank you,
Jaya Auntie,
Kamala Marmee,
but please, it's enough!
Kaarnum
Bas.'

She does not even hesitate
but simply continues to spoon
even more food
onto my plate

Unwavering in her mission
it's a condition that all aunties suffer from –
they feel the need
the need to feed

I even cover up my dish with one hand
form a line of defence with my palm and fingertips –
she will never get through this elaborate barrier
I think to myself

But little did I know
she is not afraid to pour hot sambar –
spicy, soupy
liquid gold
directly onto my skin
So at least that way
some of it can
still soak in

These daily feasts are feats of near perfection
that I have never even tried to replicate

Because feeding a family isn't easy
by any means
Hours over an open fire stove
no microwave or Uber Eats to lessen the load

And we are living in a patriarchy
naturally
so the women will wait hand and foot on the men
while they barely lift a finger
unless specifically asked
and sometimes, not even then

But I think that my Kamala Marmee
is happy, at least

She is more
joyful
than most people I know

Her laugh is a song that I would play on repeat
if I could
There's no real melody
but as she cackles and whoops
the sound fills my heart with so much joy
it could literally burst

And she is
selfless
to a degree
that I find hard to conceive

When I give her a gift
that my sister has sent to her
from across the seas
she hides it in a cupboard
for a rainy day –
or more likely
to give away to someone else
who's more in need

She is everything I wish I could be
a teacher
a mother
the most compassionate of caregivers

We stayed with her
in Vavuniya
for only four days
In a near constant
sleepy, satiated haze

There
where we were trapped in language barriers
but not when it came to food
because cooking my favourite dishes was how she said
'I love you'
every day
without fail
and that needed no further translation

Because even though it is dripping in syrup
the payasam is never too sweet
Make no mistake
it will give you cavities
and maybe a sugar induced stomach ache
but that's only for the weak –
because in my heart
it's never too sweet to eat

And the curries are never too spicy
Even when there are hot tears trailing streaks down my cheeks
and my nose threatens to run off and away
with the dish and the spoon –
they are never too spicy to try

And even when my Aunty
Marmee
asks me
finally
'Kaarnum'?
Enough?
My response to her
is a resounding –
'No'

Because even when I'm so full
that I resemble the moon
hanging low and heavy in that rusty red sky
Or a full, ripe mango
that could roll down the street
and pop like a balloon
I will never
ever
have had enough
of you

Michelle Nathan is a London-based writer and spoken word poet of Mauritian/Sri-Lankan descent. Her work often explores her relationship with her identity, family and culture as a second-generation daughter of Asian immigrants, and is almost always written while stuck on various modes of public transport. She was an Asia House Poetry Slam 2019 finalist, has had her work exhibited at the Illuminate HerStory exhibition in 2018, and printed in Dear Damsels' 2020 Annual. She currently works in children's publishing, where she hopes to help introduce the next generation to her first and greatest love: stories, in all their many, magical forms.

TOP TIP: It's going to sound obvious, but my top performing tip is to just *breathe*. Whether you're about to go on stage and are therefore (naturally) hyperventilating in the corner, or are caught like a deer in the headlights mid-poem and have no clue what the next line is, never underestimate the power of a good deep breath to help you focus, recalibrate and calm your nerves.

LITTLE MAN OF THE HOUSE

by Shagufta Iqbal

This poem is dedicated to my son, and anyone who is trying to raise a young man in this patriarchal society in which we live. It tries to rebalance the relationship we have with the environment, as we try to navigate our way back to ourselves. Essentially, it is never too late for a new beginning.

Little man of the house.
I worry about you.

Even though I know
there are many 'little mans of the house'.
Your father before you was,
my brother is,
and I'm sure my father was once too.

I worry what love looks like to you.
Quite possibly it is all hurt,
and partings,
and the grasping
at strands of what once was.

Little man of the house,
does my love suffocate you?
Your chores have doubled up,

the Hoover is your job,
the recycling too.

instead, I am trying to sit you in gardens,
push our hands into the earth,
sow seeds,
wait for sun and rain
wait for tomorrow.

We are re-learning that love is
a beautiful responsibility,
and it is patience,
and all our dreams,
in that small first sprouting
all green and fragile
against the morning light.

Founder of The Yoniverse and Kiota Bristol, **Shagufta K Iqbal** was longlisted for the 2017/2018 Jerwood Compton poetry fellowship. She is an award-winning writer, filmmaker, workshop facilitator and TEDx Speaker. Described by *gal-dem* as a poet whose work 'leaves you validated but aching – her narratives are important, heart-wrenching and relatable'. Her poetry collection *Jam Is For Girls, Girls Get Jam* has been recommended by Nikesh Shukla as 'a social political masterclass'. Her poetry film *Borders* has won several awards, and has been screened across international film festivals. She currently works in the publishing industry with Burning Eye Books, and is working on her second poetry collection and a debut novel.

TOP TIP: Speak with your audience. Performance poetry is more about honesty and authenticity and vulnerability than performance and over exaggeration. It is about starting a conversation and speaking with your community.

HASSAN II MOSQUE

by Fahad Al-Amoudi

This poem was inspired by a visit to the Hassan II Mosque in Casablanca. The French extracts were picked from bits of conversation I had with people working in and around the tourist office.

Rises out the sea,
all cedar,
and marble,
and regal,
so regal it reminds me of sandcastles
and how we prayed to the waves to preserve them,
back when I kept God on the top shelf
with nothing to hold Him down
but a thin layer of dust.

   Qu'est-ce que vous cherchez?

A little boy skates rings around the steps
like a protective charm.
He stops every now and then;
   And expects something;
He stares at the city in the distance
to make sure it's still there;

43

watches the top soil shift
like a creased prayer mat.

Ça coute cent dirhams pour les étrangers.

The security guard aims his steely glare at me.
He sits,
slumped in the shade,
cradling God in his arms
like he could drop him at any moment.
    He knows about the shelf,
        and the dust
            and how I left the back window open.

Qu'est-ce que votre origine?

When they ask for my ticket
I show them carpet burns on the hilt of my palms,
an indent on my forehead
left by a father's kiss.
The words he whispered in my ear echo through the halls,
escape through the small gap in the roof and
cascade down the walls
until they are consumed by the city.
I am lock without key,
my body is wet clay
in the lazy hands of apathy,
lying prostrate at the feet of my faith's tomb.

Tu parles l'arabe?

Under the minaret
I look at Julie like I've lost something
and she asks if I want to pray.

The sky flaps its wings,
washes over me
like *udhu*,
threads the voice of the city through my ears
and I forget what it is I have left inside.

Fahad Al-Amoudi is a poet from London currently studying History at Durham University. His work centres around grief, identity and faith with the occasional Pokémon reference. Fahad is the former captain of the award-winning Durham University Slam Team, he is a Roundhouse Poetry Slam finalist, BBC Edinburgh Fringe Slam competitor and has participated in BBC 1Xtra's Words First programme. He is part of a group called The Poetry Experiment which blends poetry with original compositions of contemporary jazz and hip-hop.

TOP TIP: Take the time to find your voice.

DUALITY

There is as much joy in being, as there is in not being. But there is sadness too. In fact, a whole gamut of emotions exists in the unnameable things — the duality here, captured in verse.

妳好/HELLO

by Jinhao Xie

Hello and *How are you?* are two of the most common phrases used in English in greetings. *Ni Hao* and *Chi Le Ma?* are two of the most common phrases used in a Chinese greeting. However, something is lost in translation. The poem uses my first encounter with people as an international living in the UK. The questions asked and the subtle prejudices are also explored. However, the poem aims to bridge and tell a story behind the facade of one's physique. It is about assimilation, misunderstandings, and the search for empathy.

Hello
When I say *Hello*
I mean 妳好, simply meaning *You good*
My acknowledgement that this is a benign encounter
And no one is getting hurt

It's me handing out an *olive branch*
I mean *cherry blossoms*
No, that's Japanese
I mean *lotus flowers*
No, I mean *I come here in peace*

When you say *Ni Hao*
You mean
Look, I have made a couple of Chinese friends at university
funny thing though, I find them everywhere in universities

I thought of learning a new language,
but my nihao is as good as my Bonjour

I don't wish to be exotic you know
So, you can begin to tell me your Far East adventure
How you 'Eat, Pray and Love'-ed your way in Asia
How you found yourself under a Bodhi Tree

It puzzles me even
How you can find yourself in my motherland
and I am lost in yours

*

So, we just carry on talking
in English
like it was nothing, but a mere Greeting

How are you?
When I say *How are you?*
I mean 吃了嗎? (Have you eaten?)

Did you have your Chicken Chow Mein?
Or Your Slice Beef in Black Bean Sauce
With a bag of Prawn Crackers?

What I want to say is
Am I the acquired taste that you find oriental initially?
Am I your friend with different coloured skin so you can say that
you are cultured?

What I really want to say is
I don't like sweet and sour
The taste is as foreign to you as it is to me

But I am still waiting
for those crucial lines
You: So . . . how long have you been here?
Me: Six years
You: *Oh, really? But your English is so good!*
Me: Thank You?!

*

Every *Thank You* translates
對不起 *(I am sorry)*
I am sorry that I have forgotten the beauty of Chinese characters
How each stroke flows like 長江水 (*the Yangzi River*)
Water runs in the veins of Chinese sons and daughters
The long history of my culture

Legends narrated in scriptures
carved in the ancient bone factures
How each stroke interlinks into strong and bold structures
And reminds me of those withered brick walls

protecting my ancestors
over millennia from intruders

*

I was sent away with my mother's prayers
She often told me that the moon shines far brighter
and is far rounder on the other side of the sea
How she has to let go of this bird
to fly for a better opportunity

Every sleepless night,
Every *A-B-C* that I have learnt is me
ripping off timbers and logs of my own language
piece by piece
I break down the monasteries of my own history
I set them on fire to keep me warm

The fire cries like a dragon that flies
and unites with the moon: home

The flame burns like feathers
鳳凰 turns to ashes
and up rises a *Phoenix*

I pour my tears on the fire
ashes to mud
I morph it into letters and spit out words
that taste like

your Sunday roasts
your Fish-n-Chips
or your English breakfast

Now, when I say *Hello*,
I sound like you

when I say *Ni Hao*
I sound like
you

Jinhao Xie is a lover of poetry and languages; is curious about the quiet voices; believes that poems carry the non-weight of hearts. Their poetry journey began in 2017. They have been telling stories through forms of poetry: on the page or spoken words. They are interested in the possibilities of existence, exploring themes of culture, gender and personhood. In early 2018, Jinhao performed a TEDx talk about searching for various meanings of Truth. Later that year, they won the inaugural Asia House Poetry Slam.

TOP TIP: Even with spoken word, 'read, read, read' is one of the most important tips I have ever received, that includes audio books, YouTube videos, films, having meaningful conversations. Don't limit yourself to just poets writing in English. Read wildly and weirdly. Perform in your own voice. Imagine how you would talk in an everyday setting and explore the variety of emotions you have. Let them be anger, confusion or ambivalence. The most important thing is to enjoy yourself because the courage you have by sharing your stories is invaluable.

SELF-PORTRAIT WITH AN IPHONE

after Will Harris

by Dean Atta

Social media became big when I was already an adult. Having a smartphone and taking selfies wasn't a part of my childhood but it is for so many now. If you choose to engage with social media you can easily begin comparing yourself to other people and that's not always healthy because you're not necessarily seeing the bigger picture.

I pay close attention to
my smile. Many are surprised

to hear of my depression,
there are no selfies of

me crying in bed. Thanks to
Tyra Banks' *America's Next Top Model,*

I have perfected the smize
– smiling with the eyes – it looks

so genuine, I could be
a top model even at rock bottom.

There will be questions:
How are you?

What are you working on?
How are things with Tom?

People only know
what I decide to share

and mostly it's glossy
as a magazine cover.

I have a positive attitude
online and when I go outside.

I prepare myself for
these interactions.

I say *I'm busy*
rather than *I'm overwhelmed.*

I say *I'm excited*
rather than *I'm anxious.*

I say *I'm in love*
rather than *I'm terrified*

of how much I depend on him
for my happiness.

When I open my mouth, I play down
what I'm feeling

behind the smile
perfected for selfies and social situations.

When I look back through all my selfies,
I believe I could be happy.

Named as one of the most influential LGBT people in the UK by the *Independent on Sunday* and 'one of poetry's greatest modern voices' by *Gay Times*, poet **Dean Atta**'s work has appeared on BBC One, BBC Radio 4, BBC World Service and Channel 4, often dealing with themes of gender, identity, race and growing up. Dean regularly performs across the UK and internationally. He is a member of Keats House Poets Forum and Malika's Poetry Kitchen, as well as beinga tutor for Arvon and Poetry School. Dean's debut poetry collection was shortlisted for the Polari First Book Prize. His latest book, *The Black Flamingo*, follows a mixed-race gay teen as he spreads his wings at university as a drag performer; a bold story about embracing your uniqueness and finding your inner strength.

TOP TIP: I write a lot of poems inspired by the work of others. Will Harris' poem 'Self-portrait in front of a small mirror' is what inspired this poem and gave me the first line: 'I pay close attention to'. So long as you acknowledge where you got your inspiration by mentioning the other author e.g. 'after Will Harris', this is not plagiarism. However, if you take a line from someone else's poem or write something similar to someone else and don't acknowledge them, that is considered plagiarism.

MOQADISHU FUNK: A HISTORY OF MIGRATION

by Amina Jama

This poem was heavily inspired by Somali culture, music and art. It follows the trajectory of 80s Somali funk music band Dur Dur and how the civil war in Somalia affected them and others.

dur dur first discovered jazz before the war   all saxophones and good vibrations
they say it sounded like the athan   the call to prayer   all intimate   they say it
sounded like a pre-wedding night   both holy and forbidden   jazz makes the
people electric   before most of the country had electricity
for a while they kept trying to smooth out the creases   like the sound was a fabric
their tendency to make everything flat   but not jazz

•

dur dur flee   some to europe   others from states to states   all   away
from home   cassette tapes are buried   along with bodies   *they should never have
started singing in the first place*   all hell breaks loose   the people think
dajjal has arrived   or iblis   they see the moon split like the land
ya'juj and ma'juj   isa descending into damascus   a cloud of smoke
yawm al qiyamah   the day of reckoning   they thought it was iblis
but it was just siad

•

dur dur are part of the diaspora   kids and grandkids   language turns from af
somali to af english   to af dutch   back to af somali but by choice this time
maxawees's are ditched   for bootcut jeans   hido iyo daqan for mini skirts
and tube tops   michael and prince are our uncles now   the moon splits again
but this time   it is like a baby opening it's eyes   to the world

•

dur dur reunite after decades and decades of statelessness   *they should never have*
stopped singing in the first place all heels are off the floor   all etiquette and shame
out the window   an invasion of colours and silk dresses   free mixing   and
twerking   mourning and celebrating   a gift of headwraps   the song talks of
burning ships on lido and berbera   smoke feels like its at our feet   they sing
about sunsets that actually touch us but feel so distance   they sing about
genoicde   grandmothers are at the front of the stage
they are back in 1980s moqadishu   tonight   these   songs   are
postage stamps commemorating the loss of their country

Amina Jama is a Somali-British writer. Barbican Young Poets
alum, member of Octavia Poetry Collective, co-host of Boxedin.
She produced and curated a touring installation and exhibition
from Aug-Dec 2019. 'Somalinimo' creates an intimate living
room space, which aims to explore the Somali experience in the
diaspora. Her debut poetry pamphlet *A Warning To The House
That Holds Me* was published in 2019 by Flipped Eye Press.

TOP TIP: Read your poems out loud in the mirror to yourself. Pay close attention to what your hands, body and face are doing whilst you're reading. Question whether these movements are intentional and what they may add to the performance of the poem.

ASK A VILLAGE GIRL

by Roshni Goyate

The village girl in this poem is my 90-something year old Aaji –
my paternal grandma. She's always lived in India so I don't get to
see her much, and in the busy-ness of life, we're not in touch a lot.
This poem explores the questions I want to ask her, and what I
imagine her responses would be – full of familiar-foreign language
and imagery, and bewilderment at the difference between her
rural Indian roots and my urban British upbringing.

Ask a village girl: How did she
Become a city dweller?
She'll tell you even after four
generations, she never left
the village. That God
brought her here. Twice a day
she roams rows of houses
called galis and nagars,
that were once a jungle,
plucking the flowers she
can reach, to make offerings.

Ask a village girl: When did
the highways appear?

She won't give you an exact
date but can say how many
devotees came to her home
to seek her blessings at
Nag Panchmi that year.
How the electricity went
and they used car headlights
to make sure all the mouths
were fed.

Ask a village girl: What does
the young widowed mother
of five look like?
She will show you her sea of
bronze snake statues, point
each one out with her fingers
made of paper bags and
ink, overgrown, stained red
at the tips with daily prayer.
She will look to them to help
heal you when you're sick.

Ask a village girl: Where does
this all end? She will close her eyes
and tell you Padmini comes to
play less and less these days
that when Padmini disappears
completely, the Gods will come and
take her. You might be stuck

underground on the Bakerloo
line, missing the old moquette,
wishing for slightly more oxygen.

Roshni Goyate is part of 4 BROWN GIRLS WHO WRITE,
who have collectively published a poetry book, a zine of essays, a
pamphlet with Rough Trade Books, and sold out their Edinburgh
Fringe show in 2019. She is the proud daughter of immigrants,
mother of Raïfi and co-founder of The Other Box.

> **TOP TIP:** My performing tip is a two-breath grounding
> technique I learned in an embodiment workshop. On the
> first inhale, imagine reaching up through the crown of
> your head and growing taller. On the exhale, root down
> with your feet, feel the weight of your body on the ground.
> On the second inhale become aware of your peripheral
> vision and the space you're in. And as you exhale, evoke an
> image in your heart that makes you smile. Mine is always
> my sister's face. I do this before any performance.

HOW NOW BROWN COW

by Sunnah Khan

This poem was inspired by the memory of a support teacher at my secondary school assuming that English was not my first language. The irony being that I was actually top of my class for English. It made me reflect on perceived versus embodied identity and what my identity means to me, compared to how others might perceive it.

Early on, I came to understand
that to align myself with English words
was to walk out free, no curfew or curry smells
chasing me down the street.

English was my bestest subject.

I'd write stories and poems
stuff them in my bag, press them
earnestly into the palms of tired teachers,
recite them on my solitary walks, to the birds
who pulled worms and listened with darting attention.

You –
told me

It was because there were some words
I just wouldn't understand.
That I couldn't possibly understand.
You –
told them
that even though I was good at *pretending*
There was something missing.

English, is not her first language.

Which one came first?
I couldn't remember.
I remember my grandfather
slapping my back, making guttural sounds
as he bounced me on his knee and I remember
the way my mother's voice sang rainbow
songs as she threw me up to touch
the sky and my forehead resting
on a prayer mat somewhere
letting the melody of that other world
reverberate in the nostrils of the Imam
and bounce around my chest.

What were the first sounds to reach my ears?
What were the first words I learnt to curl
around my tongue, that slipped from my dribbling mouth?

I imagined the beat of my mothers heart,
belly full of turqa dhal and Tunnocks tea cakes,

blood full of duty and quiet rebellion
of heartache and muttered prayers,
of hope.
So much hope.

In what language did you sing
to your swollen belly?
What colour were your tears?
Did you dream me up in Punjabi or English?
Did you seal a kiss
on my father's lips with a Persian prayer?

What language was I born of?

Sunnah Khan is a Scottish poet & documentary filmmaker living in North East London. She is part of the poetry collective 4 BROWN GIRLS WHO WRITE.

> **TOP TIP:** Centre yourself. I always try to go to yoga on the morning of a performance. I find that focussing on deep breathing and physical sensation helps me to stay out of my head and be more in my body. There's less room for fear. That really helps me to stay present with the audience when I'm on stage.

PROTEST

The language of poetry has always translated well to protest. After all, what is verse if not the fire you feel in your soul.

THIS IS NOT A HUMANISING POEM

by Suhaiymah Manzoor-Khan

I wrote this poem the day after the London Bridge attack in 2017. I was to compete in the upcoming Roundhouse slam the same week and needed a new poem. I didn't realise that this poem would change my life – garnering millions of online views and endless opportunities. Alhamdulilah.

Some poems force you to write them
the way sirens force their way through window panes in the night
and you can't shut out the news, even when you try

write a humanising poem
my pen and paper goad me
show them how wrong their preconceptions are

be relatable

Write something upbeat for a change, crack a smile
tell them how you also cry at the end of toy story 3
and you're just as capable of bantering about the weather in the
    post office queue
like everything, you have no idea how to make the perfect
    amount of pasta, still

feed them stories of stoic humour
make a reference to childhood
tell an anecdote about being frugal
mention the x factor

be domestic
successful
add layers

tell them you know brown boys who cry
about the sides of Asads, Amirs and Hassans they don't know
the complex inner worlds of Sumaiyyahs and Ayeshas
tell them comedies as well as tragedies
how full of life we are
how full of love

but no

I put my pen down
I will not let that poem force me to write it
because it is not the poem i have been reduced to

reduced to proving my life is human, because it is relatable
valuable, because it is recognisable
but good gcses, family, and childhood memories are not the only
    things that count as life
living is

So this will not be a 'Muslims are like us' poem
I refuse to be respectable.

Instead
love us when we're lazy
love us when we're poor
love us in our back-to-backs, council estates, depressed,
    unwashed and weeping
love us high as kites, unemployed, joy-riding, time-wasting,
    failing at school
love us filthy, without the right colour passports, without the
    right sounding english
love us silent, unapologizing, shopping in poundland
skiving off school, homeless, unsure, sometimes violent
love us when we aren't athletes, when we don't bake cakes
when we don't offer out homes, or free taxi rides after an event
when we're wretched, suicidal, naked and contributing nothing

love us then

Because if you need me to prove my humanity
I'm not the one that's not human

My mother texts me too after the BBC news alerts
'are you safe? let me know you're home okay?'
and she means safe from the incident, yes
but also safe from the after-effects

so sometimes I wonder
which days of the week might I count as liberal?
and which moments of forehead to the ground am i conservative?

I wonder
when you buy bombs is there a clear difference between
the deadly ones that kill
and the heroic ones that scatter democracy?

Isn't it really 'guilty, until proven innocent'?
How can we kill in the name of saving lives?
How can we illegally detain in the name of maintaining the law?

I can't write it

I put my pen away.

I can't
I won't write it

Is this radical?
Am I radical?

Because there is nowhere else left to exist now.

Suhaiymah Manzoor-Khan is Muslim, an educator, writer and
spoken word poet. She is fast becoming a leading voice interrogating
narratives around race/ism, feminism, gender, Islamophobia, state

violence and decoloniality in Britain. She is the founder and author of the critical and educative blog, www.thebrownhijabi. com, and co-author of *A Fly Girl's Guide to University: Being a Woman of Colour at Cambridge and Other Institutions of Power and Elitism* (Verve, 2019). With a background studying History and Postcolonial Studies, as well as a wider education from her mother and grandmother's wisdoms, the epistemology of Islam, and work of women of colour and anti-systemic thinkers from across the world, Suhaiymah's poetry is unapologetically political and deliberately unsettling. She isn't interested in your guesses or analyses.

Suhaiymah's poetry has over two million online views and since going viral as runner-up of the 2017 Roundhouse Poetry Slam with her poem, 'This Is Not a Humanising Poem', she has performed on BBC Radio stations, at music festivals, in the US against Californian slam poets, across British universities, on Sky TV, ITV, the Islam channel, Las Vegas, TEDxes, London poetry nights, mosques, protests outside the Home Office, in New York, Berlin and at Da Poetry Lounge in Los Angeles.

> **TOP TIP:** Don't write the poem you think people want you to write. Write the poem that you need to write. Your honesty and vulnerability are an unmatchable and unteachable force.

DEAR HEARING WORLD

by Raymond Antrobus

This is a poem I wrote after coming across a statistic that estimated 70 per cent of people born profoundly deaf in the UK grow up illiterate. I was teaching in a Hackney school at the time and quickly switched to working in deaf education. My first residency at a deaf school was in the same school I'd attended as a student in London. I recognized some of the struggles that young deaf people are still facing today and this poem is a response.

I have left Earth in search of sounder orbits,
a solar system where the space between
a star and a planet isn't empty. I have left
a white beard of noise in my place and many
of you won't know the difference. We are
indeed the same volume, all of us eventually fade.
I have left Earth in search of an audible God.
I do not trust the sound of yours.
You would not recognise my grandmother's *Hallelujah*
if she had to sign it, you would have made her sit
on her hands and put a ruler in her mouth
as if measuring her distance from holy.
Take your God back, though his songs
are beautiful, they are not loud enough.

I want the fate of Lazarus for every deaf school
you've closed, every deaf child whose confidence
has gone to a silent grave, every BSL user
who has seen the annihilation of their language,
I want these ghosts to haunt your tongue-tied hands.
I have left Earth, I am equal parts sick of your
'oh, I'm hard of hearing too' just because
you've been on an airplane or suffered head colds.
Your voice has always been the loudest sound in a room.

I call you out for refusing to acknowledge
sign language in classrooms, for assessing
deaf students on what they can't say
instead of what they can, we did not ask to be a part
of the hearing world, I can't hear my joints crack
but I can feel them. I am sick of sounding out your rules –
you tell me I breathe too loud, and it's rude to make noise
when I eat. Sent me to speech therapists, said I was speaking
a language of holes, I was pronouncing what I heard
but your judgment made my syllables disappear,
your magic master trick hearing world – drowning out the quiet,
bursting all speech bubbles in my graphic childhood,
you are glad to benefit from audio supremacy,
I tried, hearing people, I tried to love you, but you laughed
at my deaf grammar, I used commas not full stops
because everything I said kept running away,
I mulled over long paragraphs because I didn't know
what a 'natural break' sounded like, ~~you erased~~
~~what could have always been poetry~~

77

You erased what could have always been poetry.
You taught me I was inferior to standard English expression –
I was a broken speaker, you were never a broken interpreter –
taught me my speech was dry for someone who should sound
like they're under water. It took years to talk with a straight spine
and mute red marks on the coursework you assigned.

Deaf voices go missing like sound in space
and I have left earth to find them.

Raymond Antrobus was born in Hackney, London to an English
mother and Jamaican father, he is the author of *To Sweeten Bitter*
and *The Perseverance*. In 2019 he became the first ever poet to be
awarded the Rathbone Folio Prize for best work of literature in any
genre. Other accolades include the Ted Hughes award, PBS Winter
Choice, A *Sunday Times* and the *Guardian* Poetry Book of the Year
2018, as well as a shortlist for the Griffin Prize and Forward Prize.
In 2018 he was awarded The Geoffrey Dearmer Prize, (Judged by
Ocean Vuong), for his poem 'Sound Machine'. Also in 2019, his
poem 'Jamaican British' was added to the GCSE syllabus.

> **TOP TIP:** You don't want to bring too much nervous energy
> to your performance. Don't begin your poem until you feel
> ready and you can feel your audience are too. I think it's
> important to remember not to perform at them but speak
> to them.

HISTORY REMEMBERS

by Ishika Jha

This poem was inspired by a video I was watching the other day – it detailed all of Cleopatra's accomplishments and how she maintained a political hold of Egypt, and I thought, 'Wow! Why did I not know this?' And that's what got me thinking. Why is Cleopatra remembered most prominently by her relationships with two Romans, and not by the millions of other things that made her more interesting? Why is history's memory filled with so many gaps?

History remembers Cleopatra as beautiful.
That is a lie.

Statues and coins
with hooked noses
and strong features
don't show her as the 'femme fatale'
we expect to see.

Instead, Cleopatra was captivating.

Her voice,
that could speak in up to nine languages,

paired with
irresistible charm
brilliant wit
and a sharp mind,
was a weapon greater than any beauty.

She was raised with the knowledge
of the finest philosophers,
mathematicians,
scientists,
and poets of her time,
gifted with the finest education possible
in the Greek world.

As ruler,
she curbed corruption
commanded armies
sustained stability
spared grain to the poor
and strengthened her kingdom.

But her story has survived today
through the eyes of her enemies,
whispers of false rumours
and old stereotypes.

Here, they say,
rather than a protagonist in her own right,
she is a side-character

in the lives of men,
an evil seductress
who led great Romans astray.

Her enemies have succeeded.

Because before it remembers her as
a linguist,
a conversationalist,
a fleet commander,
or even a powerful ruler,

History remembers Cleopatra as beautiful.

Ishika Jha was born in London in 2004, but has lived in Newcastle for most of her life. Ever since she was little, she's been fascinated by history and fairy tales, but she's only recently gained a bigger interest in creative writing. In her free time, she draws and plays the guitar. 'History remembers' was a Foyle Young Poet commended poem. FYP is run by The Poetry Society.

> **TOP TIP:** The most important thing for me is to take your time and speak clearly, to make sure every word hits!

POPPY FIELDS AND CEDAR TREES

by Shagufta Iqbal

As a parent it can seem overwhelming to have difficult conversations about world politics and the state of the world with our children. It is easy to underestimate our children. This poem attempts to capture that moment, and how often my children have offered me a simple hope in the most difficult of times.

Beirut has often been referred to as the Paris of the Middle East.

On Sunday we remembered,
on Sunday we said never again,
lest we forget.
On Monday it was noted
that bows were not bowed enough.
That chests, red robin, were not proud enough.
On Tuesday we sold a £4 billion arms deal to Saudi Arabia.
Silence. 11 am.
On Wednesday we held our breath.
On Thursday, quietly, invisibly Beirut fell.
On Friday Paris too fell.
On Saturday refugees
ambushed by borders,

swallowed by seas,
were compared to rodents.

Fascism was never really defeated.
We will soon be at war.
We are good at war.

On Saturday my head is heavy.
On Sunday I need air.
On Sunday I walk through woods with my children.
We want to colour our hands with the redness of poppies.
Behind us we do not hear the fall of a cedar tree.

Founder of The Yoniverse and Kiota Bristol, **Shagufta K Iqbal** was longlisted for the 2017/2018 Jerwood Compton poetry fellowship. She is an award-winning writer, filmmaker, workshop facilitator and TEDx Speaker. Described by *gal-dem* as a poet whose work 'leaves you validated but aching – her narratives are important, heart-wrenching and relatable'. Her poetry collection *Jam Is For Girls, Girls Get Jam* has been recommended by Nikesh Shukla as 'a social political masterclass'. Her poetry film *Borders* has won several awards, and has been screened across international film festivals. She currently works in the publishing industry with Burning Eye Books, and is working on her second poetry collection and a debut novel.

TOP TIP: Be honest and vulnerable with your work. It requires a courage that I do not always have in my writing, but hope to learn as I continue to explore this beautiful craft.

INHERITANCE AND NEW WAYS OF LEARNING

by Zainab Dawood

I wrote this poem for a competition, the brief for which was to write a poem about Asia or the diaspora. In this piece I explore my three most-visited themes: family, culture and religion. I wanted to incorporate aspects of personal family history and relate it to the wider immigrant diaspora experience. Note: Surah Falaq is the name of one of the shortest chapters in the Quran.

You inherited the ability to be insulted.
When the drunk woman on the tube christened you
paki
you didn't react you flushed red and thought of your mother as a
    child
her bully a big white girl
who named her the same in the school playground
and all your mother could think was
'but I'm not Pakistani'

at home you placed a finger on the map and traced the journey
    from here
to religion
and further east to where you're finally just another

~~brown~~ face in the crowd
another face in the crowd
and no-one looks at you funny when you eat with your hands

on the final night you made a grieving tribute to the waves
    between the Indian Ocean and Arabian Sea
and you don't know but that might be the last of you that
    remains there because
you're the result of another person's success story
(success as defined by the criteria of a passport that is red)
and if that's what you were not then
let's be honest
you would never have picked up a pen to write poetry
nor raised your head high enough to fall in love with the land
    you were in

instead you cherish a history related through twitter
and swallow the longing in your mouth blue as Surah Falaq
but nowhere near as sweet

Zainab Dawood is a British-Indian writer from Hackney. She began writing at eighteen years old, trying her hand at short- and long-form fiction, poetry and creative non-fiction during her time at university and beyond. She enjoys attempting new artistic projects such as sketching, painting and crafting, though she doesn't spend as much time on these as she does on Netflix. Zainab spends her free time learning languages and wishing she had a pet cat.

TOP TIP: My top tip for performing is a basic one: practise, practise, practise! Unless you are a seasoned performer, I would always advise reciting your poem to yourself a few times in the mirror before you go on stage.

THE BROWN BEE SYNDROME

by Orin Begum

If there aren't enough chairs at the table then make the table bigger, never ask anybody to stand. This is the attitude I hoped I'd see when I entered the world of work. Unfortunately, what I experienced was the impact that tokenism and sexism, both at home and in the workplace, have had on young ambitious South Asian women, who have come to see each other as competition instead of allies. Through 'The Brown Bee Syndrome', I want to hold a mirror up to the false perceptions of progress South Asian women have developed over time, to make the point that progress for some is progress for none, and in a world that seeks to divide us in order to conquer us, the only way we can win is by staying united.

We are born of the Earth soaked in the blood of martyrs who
 lived and died for freedom.
So it's no wonder the politics gene found its way into our DNA
 too.

But somewhere between the Sheikh Hasinas and the Benazir
 Bhuttos and the Indira Ghandis of this
world,
our manifestos never made it to Parliament.
our campaigns never made it to the rallies.
our votes never made it to the ballot boxes.

Instead
they were cast at home, more specifically in the kitchen
because that's where our Nanis and Bibis and Ammis found that
    their electorate paid the most
attention.
Rotis and rice became the currency of power,
while empty thaalis meant a landslide victory.

You see,
our foremothers realised that the woman who
ruled the kitchen
ruled the roost
ruled the hungry men whose lifeblood came from the acrid smoke
    of that wood burning stove that
choked our voices into the backs of our throats,
and the masalas we spent generations grinding fresh every
    morning,
with the pestles we carved from our very own spines.

So when our full bellied men went off to fight the good fight
    against the enemy at the border,
they left a war zone in their wake.
Turning Wife against Mother,
woman against woman,
our sisterhood taken prisoner and our shattered bangles as
    collateral damage.

But I was told that time heals all,
so I flipped that hourglass and tried to catch the grains of sand
hoping time was something I could bend,
fast forward to the moment in the movie where we would call
    each other friend,
but I soon realised that while our constituencies can change,
    maybe we women are destined to destroy
each other in the end?

Yes we've moved out of the kitchens and
into the boardrooms, the operating theatres, the publishing
    houses,
so you'd think some things would have changed.
But our hatred for each other because of our hatred of ourselves
meant that everything stayed just the same.
We must be some sort of masochists because when we love our
    oppressors and fear our freedom,
who else can we blame?

While as doctors we women have consecrated the anatomy of
    the human body to memory,
created cures for diseases for over a century,
but who knew our Brown women politics would be so fucking
    hereditary?

Our politics clung to us like a child to its mother's sari.
Our politics grew up with us,
no longer about satisfying those who could get their leg over us,
but those who could give us a leg up,
all while adorning us with gold plated shackles that we wear with
    such pride
because our complexions look that much brighter when our wrists
    and ankles are bruised with the
colour of internalised racism masked in the guise of acceptance.

Forget breaking through glass ceilings
when you still fear cutting yourself open on my Brownness.
Fear bleeding your own true colour
because no matter how hard you scrub you will always come off
    too dark a shade of white.

There's a reason we can never the find the foundation that matches
    the colour of our skin perfectly,
because they fear we might discover the richness we evaporate into
    the atmosphere if we learn to exist unapologetically.
Fear that we might desire to be anything else but different versions
    of alabaster, porcelain or ivory.

Forget the cries for representation when you still look at me and
    see competition
instead of sister or shared hardships because, obviously, the only
    way to uplift our communities
is to eliminate our adversaries

who,
funnily enough,
just so happen to look like
you and me.

In trying to breach the borders drawn up against us by white
    supremacy,
I refuse to let our Brown women politics be passed down in my
    legacy.
Elevating you means elevating me means elevating all those
    dreams of our mothers that weren't
allowed to be.
We may have lost each other somewhere in this one-sided battle
    for equality,
but know this:
it is only when you stop hating yourself into invisibility
and dare to demand our liberty,
only then will we have won the wars that have been fought on
    the shores of our bodies for centuries.

Orin Begum is a corporate finance lawyer working for an
international law firm in London. She stumbled into poetry
during her final year reading law at the University of Oxford, as
a way to address her experiences of being a South Asian Muslim
woman in a predominately white, middle class university. Her
poetry is inspired by the struggles and strength of South Asian
women, her experiences with colourism and body shaming and
the complications of growing up as a 1.5 generation immigrant

living in a council estate in East London. She goes by the handle @poetrie_by_oreenie on Instagram.

TOP TIP: Spoken word is all about making sure each sentence, each word, each syllable lands exactly the way you want in order to evoke a certain understanding and emotion in your audience. So record yourself performing, listen back to it and ask yourself: 'Would I believe this poet if this poet was performing in front of me? Why? Why not?' And based on this make adjustments to your tone, pitch and pace.

BITTER STATE

by Duranka Perera

The attacks on Easter Sunday 2019 shook every Sri Lankan I know to the core. Watching the carnage on social media and the death toll rise, only to have to go to work the next day and pretend everything was normal . . . I don't think I'd ever felt so angry, so impotent, in so many ways. I could share a single glance with my Sri Lankan colleagues and we wouldn't need to say anything to understand how we all felt. In a heartbeat we would have sacrificed the comforts of our lives in the UK and returned to Sri Lanka to help, but of course, with sick patients to look after and limited opportunities for leave, it's not that simple. This poem then is my attempt to come to terms with how I felt in the wake of the latest blood stained episode in my country's recent history.

I was angry when it happened.
I was angry when the numbers continued to rise.
I was angry when bitter tongues lashed old wounds.
I was angry when a dying monument drew more money than
   the dying themselves.

                    I was angry when my words weren't heard.
   I was angry that I was told to watch and wait till the dust had

settled, when all I wanted was to dive right in.
I was angry that I was here, safe, distant, impotent, that the
thought of wanting to do something meant feeding my ego
before the orphaned.
I was angry that three tragedies have crushed my country in my
short lifetime.

I'm so angry that my voice is beginning to choke.
But I won't stop shouting.
So long as there is hope.

Duranka Perera is a doctor based in the East of England. After binge-watching *Avatar: The Last Airbender* in secondary school, he became bewitched by writing's capacity to create worlds, worlds rich in life and emotion, be they fantastic or otherwise. This sparked him on a journey that culminated in founding a writing society at his university, where he could and continues to bring like-minded souls together to encourage each other through their craft. His writing, enriched by his Sri Lankan heritage and strongly held belief in diversity, seeks to embody life's great variety. To him, the world is a writing sandbox: one where no story deserves to be left untold. His aspiration is to become a surgeon and author in the vein of Henry Marsh and Atul Gawande, though he is well aware that he has a long way to go before being as cool as either.

TOP TIP: I'm not the biggest fan of using emotion as a tool for creation. Peaks of emotion come too infrequently to be as reliable as cultivated discipline, but when it does come, be it in the form of anger, sadness, love, pride, fear, for anything else for that matter, write down what you feel immediately. The rawness of that feeling will often be communicated in anything you write, and it often offers the deepest insights for anyone picking up that piece of work later on.

WHEN TO WRITE

by Sophia Thakur

I'm a writer and talker. Sometimes I rhyme. Sometimes it's to music. But everytime I perform, I try to bring the audience closer to their own stories and the stories around them. Empathy. That's where my poetry starts and finishes.

When your fists are ready to paint faces
When there is nowhere to confide
When your skin lingers high above your bones
and you're so out of touch with self,
Write.
When the mouth fails you
and shyness strangles
and your throat becomes tight,
Write.
When your eyes won't dry,
Write.
Before your fight
Before you fall,
Write.
When they lie to you
When they hurt you
When they leave you,

Write.
And if they return,
And they have listened
You better write.
When the urge arises
Step out of the shower
And write.
When the world denies you
Find you power
And write.
When they speak of a freedom that doesn't include you . . .

Write away those bars
Write together your scars
Write around your wounds
Write into your womb
Write upwards
Write inwards
Write through and write around
Absolutely everything that tries to steal your sound.

Sophia Thakur is one of the most recognizable figures in UK performance poetry today. With over 14,000 YouTube followers and a rapidly growing Instagram and social media presence, Sophia has been described as 'our generation's first poetry influencer'. She combines honest and provocative lyrics, highlighting the tendencies of many hearts with contemporary music, creating something truly moving and unlike anything in the current music or poetry scene. She has collaborated with the likes of MTV, NIKE, TEDx, BET and performed her work at some of the UK's biggest music festivals and venues (Glastonbury, Lovebox, Roundhouse, Tate Britain and many more.) In 2018 she signed a major book deal with Walker Books who released her first poetry collection *Somebody Give This Heart A Pen* in October 2019 across Europe and Australia, and across the United States in January 2020.

TOP TIP: Decide who the poem is before you get on stage. Does it whisper, shout, walk around? Is is confident, is it sexy, is it curious? Become it.

TO LGBT RUSSIA WITH LOVE

by Dean Atta

At the time of writing this poem I had seen a lot of news about the Russian gay propaganda law, which prohibits adults from telling children about the existence of LGBT people. This made me think of Section 28, a law the UK government introduced in 1988 to prohibit the promotion of homosexuality by local authorities. It meant that most schools were afraid to teach anything about LGBT people. This law was in place the whole time I was at school and was only stopped in 2000 in Scotland and 2003 in the rest of the UK.

They create hate
to separate
and scapegoat us
wherever we are.

From Russia to Nigeria,
the Kremlin to the National Assembly,
the law denies us equality.

To be attacked
or beaten in the street
is a part of our reality.

Even here in the UK
that has happened to me.

Where there are laws to protect
doesn't make us free to express
who we were born to be.

Whether you are L, G, B or T,
we are a community, by necessity.
When any one of us is persecuted
we should all take it personally.

We are a family;
dysfunctional like all the rest,
not the worst and not the best,
not cursed and not blessed.

Just people
who deserve to be equal
because we all are.
Just people.
Teachers, doctors, engineers,
athletes, actors, not poofs and queers,
not trannies, not faggots, not dykes,
just human beings
with human rights.

If I say your country
would be poorer without you

and your life would be richer
elsewhere, is that fair?
Because if your country has your heart,
who am I to tell you to leave?

We have to be
the change we want to see,
not hide or run but overcome.

And yes it's easy for me to say
here in the UK;
I don't have to live in fear everyday,
so I wouldn't blame you
if you didn't stay.

From Moscow, Russia, to Kingston, JA,
I don't know what I'd do
in your position.
All I've done here is sign a petition,
write a poem and tweet about it.
It's not enough.

How will this keep you going
when it gets so tough
you consider taking your own life?
Looking at a gun,
a rope or a knife
like an exit sign
out of this hell that you're living in.

What would my words mean then,
when you're so close to giving in
because of tireless hate
abuse and rejection.

This poem
cannot provide you any protection
but it might
remind you that you are not alone.

Brothers and sisters,
your struggle is known,
all over the world
this family is growing,
with straight allies too,
until one day
those you fight will stand by you.

Named as one of the most influential LGBT people in the UK
by the *Independent of Sunday* and 'one of poetry's greatest modern
voices' by *Gay Times*, poet **Dean Atta**'s work has appeared on BBC
One, BBC Radio 4, BBC World Service and Channel 4, often
dealing with themes of gender, identity, race and growing up.
Dean regularly performs across the UK and internationally. He is a
member of Keats House Poets Forum and Malika's Poetry Kitchen,
as well as being a tutor for Arvon and Poetry School. Dean's debut
poetry collection was shortlisted for the Polari First Book Prize.
His latest book, *The Black Flamingo*, follows a mixed-race gay teen

as he spreads his wings at university as a drag performer; a bold story about embracing your uniqueness and finding your inner strength.

TOP TIP: When you address a poem to a real or imaginary audience, it can help you figure out the tone in which to write it. I imagined I was writing this poem to LGBT people being persecuted in Russia and I knew I wanted the poem to be compassionate, encouraging and convey solidarity. I use the word 'we' to connect myself to this particular audience. I also ask some rhetorical questions that serve to make the poem feel more like it's a conversation. Obviously, this poem will be read by people who are not Russian and do not identify as LGBT but addressing a poem to a particular person or group doesn't mean others won't be able to understand and appreciate it.

DESIRE

What is life without the beauty of desire? Desire that drives us to love louder, to want more, and to follow our hearts until we actualize our dreams. It's the words our hearts whisper to us. Words you will find on the following pages.

MY DUA IS LOVE

by Sanah Ahsan

'My Dua Is Love' translates as my prayer is love. It explores my continually evolving and growing understanding of prayer. I am learning that love in all its forms, including sex and intimacy, can be prayer in itself. This offering of my truth may give some insight into the journey I continue to travel in seeking nearness to God. It has been a brave, liberating and tender movement away from externally imposed societal narratives of shame, towards rewriting the inner script of my life with love and radical self-acceptance. This piece is both a celebration and remembrance of God's unconditional love and presence, interweaved with the love shared between two Queer South Asian Womxn.

i am learning that the desire is not dirty. that i need not pray
    myself clean.
that shame need not shove me to my knees
forehead to zameen
to bring me closer to my deen

my dua is love.
my dua is love.

it pours pure
like zamzam
through my body
    through her body
through my body
    through her body

we are holy.
we are holy in liquid sighs and sweat soaked skin.
i cannot tell where she ends and i begin
as love interweaves through estuaries of limb
in this tapestry of brown

it is not a sin.
it is not a sin
instead
a call to prayer.

it is a call to prayer
whenever my name leaves her lips with devotion
i know that god is here

whenever i am with her
i know that god is here.

Sanah Ahsan is a Queer Pakistani Muslim Womxn, trainee clinical psychologist, reporter, spoken word artist and published poet. She is also active in social justice and community spaces.

Sanah recently presented 'Young, British and Depressed,' a Channel 4 *Dispatches* documentary on mental health, as well as giving a TEDx talk on how we can use poetry to develop self-compassion.

Her poetry performance journey began with BBC 1Xtra's Words First, and has taken her to the stage of Shakespeare's Globe Theatre. She recently won the Outspoken Prize 2019 in the performance poetry category for this piece 'My Dua Is Love.'

Sanah works closely with grassroots organisation Jawaab in tackling Islamophobia, and her activism has involved collaborating with organisations such as Human Appeal and Childline. She is currently conducting research to deconstruct whiteness within clinical psychology, whilst developing community projects promoting further dialogue around QTIPOC, young people's mental health, and spaces for queer muslim womxn.

> **TOP TIP:** Labour with love and brave vulnerability to offer the exact utterance of your truth – a truth that needs to be heard. Each expression you offer creates a world in itself! Come as you are.

LET ME COUNT THE WAYS

by Sheena Patel

Sometimes tiny, ordinary moments can combust into profound feelings. I like the discombobulation of the two, that life can deliver.

These are the ways you make me feel:
one ice cube clinking in a wine glass on a hot day
overfilling my mouth with my mum's food
   when I haven't been home in a while
every hair on my head lifting in anticipation
my first sip of coffee
confident muscles stretching before a perfect dive bomb into
   a cool, blue pool in front of the lifeguards and a sign that says:
   no dive bombing
family, but the one you choose
a high note on a violin
the absolute joy at meeting a freshly-wrought human being
   by someone you love
the split second of the heart leap when you're swinging
   on a swing at the upswing before gravity claims you
bliss at dancing your hardest to good techno and you look around
   and everyone is beautiful
the cranium split when you think a completely new thought
   and the world rushes in

thick snow over everything familiar

the searing burn from sitting too close to a fire.

Sheena Patel is a poet and part of the collective, 4 BROWN GIRLS WHO WRITE. Sheena lives and works in London.

> **TOP TIP:** You have to truly believe that you deserve to be there, standing in front of people and taking up their attention. 'You deserve to be here' is what I say to myself before I go on. This thought slows me down, helps me put pauses in when I read and take a breath. It helps hugely that I have my sister-poets next to me, saying the same thing. It's a beautiful echo. So I'll say it to you: it is necessary for us to hear your words, you deserve to be here. Take up the space!

EVERYTHING I NEVER ASKED HIM

by Nikita Gill

This poem is about how asking the right questions can make such a difference to a relationship. It's about masculinity, desire and hope for anyone who has had a question at the edge of their tongue they are too afraid to ask.

How often do you tell
your mother that you love her.
How often has your father
held you and let you cry.

Did you ever love a soul
you always knew would never love you back.
Did you ever love a man fiercely enough
to hold him close yet not name him brother.

Can you speak of the first girl who broke your heart
without calling her something cruel too.
Can your heart ever heal from the things
you will never tell me were done to you.

Is there a worship inside you
that calls to the forgotten forgiveness in you.
Is there a sacred you wish someone understood,
a sweeter language you wish someone else knew too.

Have your fingers known fists
before they knew the openness of holding hands.
Has your skin known bruises
before it has known the tenderness of touch.

What would you be the God of.
What would you be the God of.

If they made you
a God of soft things
would you finally learn gentle
in ways it was withheld from you.

Nikita Gill is a British-Indian writer and artist living in the South of England. With a huge online following, her words have captivated hearts and minds all over the world. Nikita is an ambassador for National Poetry Day and is a regular speaker at literary events.

TOP TIP: Just remember the audience is there to watch you succeed. They're rooting for you with every word you say. All you need to do is speak your truth.

LOVE, IN THE MOVIES

by Sarah Nazir

Ladies and gentlemen, what the rom-coms will not tell us is that time moves and love fades. But in spite of that, I present to you my first published poem, for what is penned on paper – or spoken aloud, indeed – does not spoil in face of that 'unremembering'. Inspired by my lasting love of movies and the company of my best friend, I present to you: 'love, in the movies'.

sometimes i'm afraid we're just a little too good to be true
a little too daydream-fantasy-come-to-life;
a cheesy chick-flick with the quiet girl and the dreamy boy
– every film critic's worst nightmare and a film we'd never watch.
sat in that coffee shop in Cambridge on that June morning,
the air heavy with moisture and superficial comfort
i bet we're a sight to behold. outside, humid air shifts
at the sigh of an infrequent wind, etches leaf-blown cursives
into a world that seems to thirst for sickly sweet poetry.
from this side of the glass the crowds are goldfish in a tank:
shiny, slippery, volatile as they restlessly weave in
and out of one another, their ruckus a pale sound
against the rhythm of your easy breaths as you gently doze.
i bet any good composer could make music out of you.
in the real world, that burdensome air would render touch foreign,

quietly from delicacy to prickly nuisance and yet
my head rests perfectly in the crook of your neck,
as if we were two pieces of a jigsaw puzzle finally in place.
as is the common cliché, time seems to hang still
long enough for me to memorise every fold of your knuckle
as your hand sits languidly in mine, long enough
for every particle of glowing air to settle in our seams,
seemingly bind us together forever. I wait
for the sound of the clapperboard or the director's call or
for you to stir and rise and exit, but it does not come.
for now, i'll settle for this daydream,
mark it in place in my memory, forget to anticipate
our imminent untangling, that graceless separation
as the light hardens and everything becomes a little too real.

Born and raised in Lahore, **Sarah Nazir** moved to the UK at the age of seven where she learned and fell in love with English – and all the poetry that came with it. She began actively writing poetry and anonymously publishing them online age thirteen, before coming to the crude realisation that none of her work was as great as she'd previously thought. After a period of revaluation, reconsideration and opening herself up to the criticism of loving but harsh friends, she considered publishing her poems for real. 'love, in the movies' is her first published poem at age sixteen and certainly not her last. It is a Foyle Young Poet commended poem. FYP is run by The Poetry Society. For age twenty-six, Plan A is to become an artist that makes lasting impressions on the lives of her readers. *Et si defectum*, Plan B is to become a doctor that makes lasting impressions on the lives of her patients. In the meantime, you may find Sarah in between completing a handful of poems (some good, most bad), trying (and slightly failing) to understand chemistry but mostly just watching neo-noir films and calling it 'research' for something or other.

TOP TIP: I know lots of amazing public speakers and even the best of them trip up since it's inevitable in what is sometimes a high-pressure situation with audiences that aren't too accommodating at times. In those times, it's best to take a breath, move on and not take yourself too seriously. God knows how many times it's worked for me.

LET'S TALK ABOUT THE WEATHER

by Christy Ku

Okay, this poem isn't really about the weather. My combined upbringing in both British and Asian cultures has resulted in me being supremely awfully terrible at talking about desire or sensuality or that sort of thing. This poem is my attempt to start these discussions and to remind myself that it's more than fine to ask for tenderness without apologies.

show me a slow storm.
pull the air pressure down,
build a humidity that beads
crystals on skin.

lower the temperature.
give me nights so cold
sighs linger on glass.

bring me rain
trailing long rivers
edged with streetlights
every trace silver and amber.

let lightning shiver across the sky.

afterwards
when clouds have parted,
all we'll see are stars.

Christy Ku is an up-and-coming London-based multimedia creative. She is a Barbican Young Poet alum, one of the top six finalists for BBC 1Xtra's Words First programme 2019 and has headlined nights across the country. Christy is also a short story writer, YouTube journalist, digital content producer, photographer and podcaster. She is currently working towards her debut poetry collection and various other projects.

TOP TIP: Ask yourself; how do the words feel? How do they sit in or on your body, your face, your hands, your mouth? As a result, how do you carry them? How do you give those words to the audience?

ACCEPTANCE

Perhaps the greatest accomplishment of a successful person is how to master the art of acceptance. To know how to value yourself for the things no one values you for as much as the attributes everyone loves you for. This final section of the book is a masterclass on how to love yourself for who you truly are.

A SPICE

by ChefAdoniz

I'm known as Mr Master of sauce. I specialize in English and French fine dining as a chef, but words and poetry are the recipes and the ingredients of my journey. What I bring is flavour and seasoning to topics not typically covered. We all need a bit of salt and pepper for the palate of poetry, just like we do in the kitchen. This poetry is soul food . . . let me feed you some ideas. You never know what will be taken away for digestion when you're dealing with ChefAdoniz . . .

When a man calls you hot
He doesn't even know
What kind of spice you are.
You got flavour flowers ain't gonna cut this when you're a herb I
    got thyme for.

I'm feeling your spirit
Smoking without needing the sage.
Can see the heritage all in your age.
Let me tell you what lies in your ingredients
I got on this page.

123

Missing an Anise Angelic Allspice.
The coriander seeds gets carry'ed a way
Bare tings in this rice.
I put a spoon in as this is more than nice.
All my Baes leaf.

Lots come at you salty
Hence why you're a black pepper.
Hard to stop the black Cumin.
Some of us need to taste mace.
When I see you as more than a hole
And something I want to nutmeg.

Have most choking on the thought of . . .
Swallowing you miss cinnamon
See the brightest and shine in your complexion
Feeling a hint of Turmeric.
Some be on you like porsha get it from you like cayenne.

Tongue dipped in paprika
Miami had ball games as if heat
Behind those words.
You're a different kind of stock.
No Oxo cube

Times I bought Rose for a Mary . . .

Times I bought Rose for a Mary . . .
You're looking alot of different from hair to ankle you must be a
    5 spice.
Like most herbs you come at a price.
Most can't keep you have them on a sprint.
Well I find you refreshing
Like Moroccan mint.
Maybe we should chill sleep on this one
Chamomile.
Not one to act first have me thirsty for your
sorrel

Like from the garden of Eden you was picked.
The kind of herb or spice
Natural and fragrant
Most wanted to try
Have you bagged
on the freshness.

Next time he calls you hot see if he can handle the chilli before
    he flakes.
Still ask myself where has Tara Gone . .
See you as saffron
You're for more than a season.

Sweet aromatic flavour Rich without Reason.

Natives don't get our language or customs as if Asian.

Add spice to a dish cusines as if Cajun.

From ginger to vanilla

Lavender the scent of your perfume

Without medicine is a killa.

You're a Spice special flavour as if Food.

Question what kind of Spice are U

Duban C Sinclair is a Capricorn hailing from South London Caribbean parents and is the oldest of six. Creating is his saviour and food his muse; he is an extroverted introvert who performs and writes under his alter ego ChefAdoniz. He specializes in English and French fine dining in an array of environments working with celebrity chefs and masters of their craft and has been a chef for thirteen years. It is this intensely creative, constantly shifting setting that fuels his expression. That and the support of his best friends, including #1, his mum. ChefAdoniz has been writing since he was a young teenager.

> **TOP TIP:** Timing is everything!
> - Give the room time to breathe, to digest and savour your words.
> - Breathe and remember you're in control of time. You pace your art the way you feel is best. It's the way it was intended – it's your world to show when you want and how you want.

THINGS I WISH I COULD TRADE MY HEADSCARF FOR

by Fathima Zahra

This poem draws on the lived experiences of my family and I as one of the few Muslim families living in a small town in Essex, having recently migrated from Jeddah.

A fishbowl/ a space helmet/ a tin foil hat/ bubble wrap/ a shoe box/ a handful of snakes/ and it will still / be the least suspicious thing/ in a train carriage/ this country sings/ of all the ways it loves us/ in the soft slip/ of hate mail through our front door/ how eyes under furrowed brows/ walk me down the aisle in tube carriages/ how men flip us off/ as my dad drives me to the train station/ how a face peers out/ window rolled down to scream/ MUZLIM! / and I think, yes? / I am? / my scarf speaks parseltongue now/ eggs spectators on/ as if to say/ 'here is an empty goalpost/ kick those slurs in' / I didn't sign up for this/ when at twelve/ my mum brought me pretty scarves/ to grow into someday

Fathima Zahra is an Indian poet currently based in Essex. She is a Barbican Young Poet and a Roundhouse Poetry Collective alum. Her work has been featured across BBC World News, the *New Indian Express* and Young Poets Network. She has won the

Bridport Prize, Wells Festival of Literature Young Poets Award and Asia House Poetry Slam 2019. In her work, she tends to explore the lives of the diaspora and what belonging means to her. She is currently studying towards a Biomedical Sciences degree at Queen Mary University of London.

TOP TIP: With poems that come from a place of rage and frustration, it's quite easy to tap into the emotion and get carried away. Anger doesn't always look like yelling and wild hand gestures. Practise restraint, the punches land harder in the heavy silence after each line.

BODY CONVERSATION

by Tanaka Fuego

This is a poem which is distinct and personal to my experience with my body, following the notion of how others speak of you/to you and how it can then become internalised. This poem is about breaking the negative and unhealthy narrative with one's body.

If my body could speak
I think it would sound like my mother
Full of disappointment, with a pinch of hope
Holding on to some faint idea that I might be able to love
myself again

If my body could speak
I think it would sound like my brother
Full of resentment, and pain
But not have a clue how to express it
So I think it would yell

If my body could speak
I think it would say things
Only my father
Could hold in his arsenal
Expecting everything
After doing barely anything

If my body could speak
I think it would give me the silent treatment
Just like my sister
Cause if you haven't got nothing
Nice to say
Then you shouldn't say anything at all

Fun fact:
When I was 9
Every night I would pray . . .
For this body
To just instantaneously combust
Praying for it to start a fire in my mother's home
Forcing her to finally realise I've been burning alive this whole
    time
But I guess god didn't even think these bones were worthy of
    being dry wood

Yesterday I thought
If I could have a healthy dialogue with this body
I wouldn't even know where to start
But I would mumble an attempt at
I'm sorry
For binding and bruising these ribs
For not thinking it was worth a glance in the mirror
I would apologise
For all the glances of disgust I've given it in the mirror
I would beg for forgiveness
Grovel at the shrine which is this vessel

And make jewels out of all the tears and slurs I have spewed at it

Being a living testimony that a flower can bloom even in a
   darkroom

I would hope

And I would even pray

That my body would accept the apology

Grace me with a smile and

Maybe . . . just say that it loves me still

Tanaka also known as Tanaka.fuego is a slam-winning, multi-published, international spoken word artist, who has performed to sold-out shows at Edinburgh's Fringe festival. He is a BBC 1xtra Words First alum and a Roundhouse Poetry Slam finalist, alongside being commissioned by the BBC. He is a Black queer artist whose poems cross leaps and boundaries throughout his Identity.

TOP TIP: Speak with conviction and all will be fine.

TEEN GIRL

by Neha Agrawal

This is one of those rare poems that I just sat down and wrote in one go. There was minimal editing. I think it comes from a feeling of having to behave a certain way to be one of society's 'teen girls' . . . the inner voice versus the outer voice.

here i am

in-side your thoughts / detached
i swear i can see myself

> *this is some perennial substitute reality*
> *i think i'd rather like to stay here please*

in the sainsbury's parking lot holding
your hand & a balloon
hiding from: responsibility / growing too fast /
and such

> *frankly, lipstick scares me / all those aggressive reds and oranges*

in a fix please help please i've lost my phone / my keys / my real
      face

> *in-terestingly i'm slowly losing knowledge of who's fake / who's not*
> *don't you see you can't see through them at first glance*

in-destructive & in-vincible & in-eradicable
when i want to be

> *in pain but i don't think anybody wants to see more hurt*
> *in-tolerable & too sensitive but i try not to be*

in between the lines of your newspaper
if you're looking / if you read closely enough

in the screen of your phone / computer / tv / pick one
i'll be: the news presenter / acerbic / the journalist /
that sexy one in the tight dress
you'll remember me
you'll love me
i promise
i swear

> *are you sure though*
> *d'you really think i'm good enough?*

Poetry is **Neha Agrawal**'s passion. For her, the words are important, but so is the structure, the syntax and the shape of the poem on the page and how it reads in front of an audience. Neha's other interests are rowing out on the Tideway and she is currently designing an educational website. She wants to study Biology, Chemistry, Maths and English Literature at A-level. 'Teen Girl' was a Foyle Young Poet commended poem. FYP is run by The Poetry Society.

TOP TIP: You have to express your heart in your voice. There's no mind involved here.

TINNITUS

by Esin Aynal

This poem is about a condition I have called tinnitus, when a person hears noises such as ringing, whirring or whistling through their ears. I wrote this poem to show that even a small noise has the terrible power of making people feel alone in their struggles. In my case, I would miss silence and the ability to fall asleep without hearing that ringing in my right ear. But through the help of my loving parents, Mehmet, time and my portable radio playing as I fall asleep, I've grown to accept that little voice in my ear. I want those with tinnitus to know that they are not alone.

Tinnitus is the name the doctor has given
to the whirring sound in my right ear,
which so fondly plays the same tune in my
head
over and over and over again
At night when all is silent and dark,
I can hear its voice once more before I sleep,
a loud squeal going up and down
a rubber balloon slowly deflating
the crunchy rumble of a broken tv
Instead of annoyance at this constant tornado whirl swirling in
    my ear,

I felt only loneliness,
at how I was the only one who could hear its petrifying squeal
the cracked voice of angel
screaming in the night
It is incurable, they say,
just learn to live with it.
So I play it some radio every night as I fall asleep,
so the minuscule sound in my right ear
won't have to sing alone in the night.

Esin Aynal is a sixteen year old student from East London, who spends her days reading books at an alarmingly fast pace, painting ridiculous portraits and *attempting* to study. She also writes poetry at those special times when she feels people aren't listening! 'Tinnitus' was a Foyle Young Poet commended poem. FYP is run by The Poetry Society.

TOP TIP: A tip I keep with me when performing at slams is to perform with passion and rhythm! Performing gives you that great opportunity to really make people listen to your words and story. Be expressive with your hands and face, and reach out towards the audience, visualise yourself pulling them by the ear, shouting 'listen!'

THE GUY MY PARENTS WANT ME TO MARRY ASKS ME TO DESCRIBE MYSELF

by Nikita Gill

In India we have a system of arranged marriage which still plays an important part in the culture. It's so important that people ask 'was yours a love marriage or arranged?'. Years ago, when my parents were introducing me to men they thought were the right match for me, parts of this poem began to form. It finally came into fruition this year as a whole.

Look, I'm a commitment-phobe.
And this isn't my fault.
This is because people are generally crap.
Too many lovers who have insisted
they loved me have left the hot water
running too long in my house
and not cared about the planet
the very specific way I do or voted Tory
or told me my aloo gobi isn't great
(and I'll have you know
it's bloody brilliant)
or not cared for red wine and—

sorry, what I'm trying to say is don't worry.
I'm not due to fall in love till 2024 anyway,
my tarot cards told me so.
I mean, if you believe in that kind of thing.
I mean, it's not wild that I check
my horoscope every morning is it?
Or that I know I'm a Gemini sun,
Aries moon, Capricorn rising?
And if the day is going to be
bad for any of those three signs,
I carry red jasper in my right pocket
for anxiety and an amethyst in my bra
to dispel bad luck.

None of this is weird.
I know because my tarot cards told me so.
But really, the best way to get to know me
is not to read the poetry.
Don't follow me on Instagram.
And for god's sake
definitely don't visit my twitter.
You see, women like me,
we are made from a different kind of mud.
We watched our mothers wear silence
instead of mouths for so long,
followed religions that told them
that women are always smaller
than the men in their lives,

we didn't have a choice but to grow these repressed voices into
    howls in our bellies,
let them swell and tumble out as jagged opinions.

We built skyscrapers instead of castles,
read Audre Lorde instead of William Wordsworth,
Bell Hooks instead of Mahatma Gandhi, sharpened our own
    bones into knife points
just in case we needed to weaponise our bodies and . . . and it
    doesn't stop there.
You see, those are the better parts.
You see, hiding pain as courage
is what all good wolves do.
I have named harsh hands home.
I have stumbled after women
who could not decide
if I was an experiment or a forever.

I have been a scarlet woman for so long,
I cannot even remember his name.
Just the red letter he left on my mind.
You need a cast iron stomach to digest me.
Which is to say that I don't think
there is anyone in this world
who can survive me.
Which is to say:
sometimes you need to leave
wild things just the way
you found them.

Alone.

Nikita Gill is a British-Indian writer and artist living in the South of England. With a huge online following, her words have captivated hearts and minds all over the world. Nikita is an ambassador for National Poetry Day and is a regular speaker at literary events.

> **TOP TIP:** Humour is a great way to relate to your audience your set. It also relaxes you to hear people laughing with you and gives you a boost of instant confidence.

SPACE

by Sharan Hunjan

As a teacher I've noticed that we impose stereotypes on young people and they try to fulfil them. In my school sometimes the young brown girls were seen as the quiet, shy ones and this poem is to show them, and others who feel silenced, that they can break these stereotypes and that there is a space for them to be heard.

Why are you so quiet
Why do you shrink like you don't belong

This space is not big enough to hold you
You and me and them and you, you
Shrink
Shrink like a lotus flower lost
In a dead spring
Lost and you shrink

This space is not for you

They ask
Why are you so quiet
Why have you learnt from others

From unsaid unmoving words
That you should sit quietly
Wait your turn
Let others take that space

Did no one tell you
Space is infinite

Space is yours for the taking
Space is a void
It is a boundless bountiful beautiful space
Where the stars dust and twist and turn

In their space so take your space
Quiet brown girl
It is not white
Despite what they might make you think
In fact, it is black

In this dark matter
Of space
Take it and run
Run or jump or shout or fly
See how far you can take this space
And you will see that when you close your eyes
The dark space is there
Is mine
Is yours
Is ours

Stand
Shoulders back
Face forward
Eyes fixed like dark planets
Revolving evolving
Involving you
Take this space
It is yours.

Own it.

Sharan Hunjan is part of the collective, 4 BROWN GIRLS WHO WRITE who have released a book of poetry and a zine. She has a pamphlet published with Rough Trade Books. She is a Secondary English teacher and lives in London.

TOP TIP: Take your time and don't be afraid of silences.

THANKS

This book has been such a fulfilling manifestation of love. I want to thank every single poet who contributed and gave me the privilege of reading their splendid work. Honestly, to exist and share an era with you is such an honour.

A huge thank you to Simran Sandhu, whose tireless hard work and positivity has made this book and process so joyful. I could not have done it without you, Sim.

Thank you to Gaby Morgan, who made this book a possibility, you are a star!

Massive thanks to Pan Macmillan for publishing this, my friends and housemates for enduring my madness whilst I put this together and finally, to you, dear reader, for joining us on this magical journey told through verse.

It has been a true pleasure. Thank you.

ACKNOWLEDGEMENTS

Agrawal, Neha: 'Teen Girl' is a Foyle Young Poet commended poem by Neha Agrawal. Copyright © Neha Agrawal. Used with kind permission of The Poetry Society, and the author. **Ahsan, Sanah:** 'My Dua is Love' by Sanah Ahsan. Copyright © Sanah Ahsan. Used with kind permission of the author. **Al-Amoudi, Fahad:** 'Hassan II Mosque' by Fahad Al-Amoudi. Copyright © Fahad Al-Amoudi. Used with kind permission of the author, with special thanks to Apples and Snakes. **Antrobus, Raymond:** 'Dear Hearing World' by Raymond Antrobus from *The Perseverance* (Penned in the Margins, 2018). Copyright © Raymond Antrobus. Used with kind permission of the author and the publisher. **Atta, Dean:** 'Self-portrait with an iPhone' and 'To LGBT Russia with Love' by Dean Atta. Copyright © Dean Atta. Used with kind permission of the author. **Aynal, Esin:** 'Tinnitus' is a Foyle Young Poet commended poem by Esin Aynal. Copyright © Neha Agrawal. Used with kind permission of The Poetry Society, and the author. **Begum, Orin:** 'The Brown Bee Syndrome' by Orin Begum, first published in *Words By* (Suitcase Media International, 2019), ed. Sophie Mackenzie, Bethany Gill, Noura Al-Maashouq. Copyright © Orin Begum. Used with kind permission of the author. **Cabida, Troy:** 'Not dying for London' from *War Dove* (Bad Betty Press, 2020) by Troy Cabida. Copyright © Troy Cabida. Used with kind permission of the author. **ChefAdoniz:** 'A Spice' by ChefAdoniz. Copyright © Duban Sinclair. Used with kind permission of the author. **Dawood, Zainab:** 'inheritance and new ways of learning' by Zainab Dawood. Copyright © Zainab Dawood. Used with kind permission of the author. **Fetuga, Rakaya:** 'Box' by Rakaya Fetuga. Copyright © Rakaya Fetuga. Used with kind permission of the author. **Fuego, Tanaka:** 'Amongst the smog' and 'Body Conversation' by Tanaka Fuego. Copyright © Tanaka Fuego. Used with kind permission of the author. **Goyate, Roshni:** 'Ask a Village Girl' from *4 Brown Girls Who Write* (FEM Press, 2018) by Sharan Hunjan, Sunnah Khan, Sheena Patel and Roshni Goyate. Copyright © Roshni Goyate. Used with kind permission of the author. **Grover, Aman:** 'Lost in Translation' by Aman Grover. Copyright © Aman Grover. Used with kind permission of the author. **Hunjan, Sharan:** 'Space' from *4 Brown Girls Who Write* (FEM Press, 2018) by Sharan Hunjan, Sunnah Khan, Sheena Patel and Roshni Goyate. Copyright © Sharan Hunjan. Used with kind permission of the author. **Iqbal, Shagufta:** 'Poppy Fields and Cedar Trees' from *Jam is For Girls, Girls Get Jam* (Burning Eye Books, 2017) and 'Little Man of the House' by Shagufta Iqbal. Copyright © Shagufta Iqbal. Used with kind permission of the author. **Jama, Amina:** 'moqadishu funk: a history of migration' by Amina Jama. Copyright © Amina Jama. Used with kind permission of the author, with special thanks to Barbican Young Poets. **Jha, Ishika:** 'History Remembers' is a Foyle Young Poet commended poem by Ishika Jha. Copyright © Ishika Jha. Used with kind permission of The Poetry Society, and the author. **Jiang, Xinyue:** 'my city and i' a Foyle Young Poet commended poem by Xinyue Jiang. Copyright © Xinyue Jiang. Used with kind permission of The Poetry Society, and the author. **Khan, Sunnah:** 'How Now Brown Cow' from *4 Brown Girls Who Write* (FEM Press, 2018) by Sharan Hunjan, Sunnah Khan, Sheena Patel and